Bugs in Bed

Written by Jillian Powell

Illustrated by Jimothy Oliver

Dad and Tom get the kit.

Tom taps the pegs.

Dad tugs and tugs the top.

Dad rips the top!

The sun sets on the hill.

Tom gets into bed.

Bugs go in the gap.

The bugs nip Dad and Tom!

Tom tucks a sock in the gap.

The bugs go back!

Talk about the story

Ask your child these questions:

1 What did Tom do to the pegs?

2 What did Dad do to the top of the tent?

3 How did the bugs get into the tent?

4 Why did Tom chase the bugs out of the tent?

5 How would you get rid of bugs in your tent?

6 Would you like to go camping? Why/why not?

Can your child retell the story using their own words?